RUSH DRUMS

ON THE CD: FIRST VERSION OF SONG IS THE FULL DEMONSTRATION TRACK,
THE SECOND VERSION IS THE BACKING TRACK TO PLAY ALONG TO

First published by Faber Music Ltd in 2009
Bloomsbury House 74–77 Great Russell Street
London WC1B 3DA

Arranged by Noam Lederman
Engraved by Tom Fleming
Edited by Lucy Holliday

Guitar by Tom Fleming
Bass by Neil Williams
Drums by Noam Lederman
Synth Programming by Tom Fleming
Recorded at the Limehouse, London
www.thelimehouse.com
Engineered by Alan Thomson
Mixed by Alan Thomson & Tom Fleming
www.tomflemingmusic.co.uk

Noam plays Mapex, Paiste & Protection Racket

Designed by Lydia Merrills-Ashcroft

Printed in England by Caligraving Ltd

The text paper used in this publication is a virgin fibre product that is manufactured in the UK to ISO 14001 standards. The wood fibre used is only sourced from managed forests using sustainable forestry principles. This paper is 100% recyclable

ISBN10: 0-571-53243-8
EAN13: 978-0-571-53243-8

To buy Faber Music publications or to find out about the full range of titles available, please contact your local music retailer or Faber Music sales enquiries:

Faber Music Ltd, Burnt Mill, Elizabeth Way,
Harlow, CM20 2HX England
Tel:+44(0)1279 82 89 82
Fax:+44(0)1279 82 89 83
sales@fabermusic.com fabermusic.com

ANTHEM

Music and Lyrics by Geddy Lee, Alex Lifeson and Neil Peart

19
22
♩. = 146
24
4
29
32
35
37
E
C
1. Know your place in life is where you want to be, don't
2. Live for your - self, there's no - one else more
Vary fills on repeat

39
D
E
let them tell you that you owe it all to me.
worth liv - ing for.
Keep on look - ing for-ward, no
Beg - ging hands and bleed -
42
C
D
E
use in look-ing 'round, hold your head a-bove the ground, it won't bring you down.
- ing hearts will on - ly cry out for more.
45
G
A
C
D
An - them of the heart and an - them of the mind,
a fu - ne - ral dirge for
48
E
G
A
eyes gone blind.
We mar - vel af - ter those who sought
51
C
Daddll
C
Daddll
C
Daddll
won - ders in the world,
won - ders in the world,
won - ders in the world they
choke
choke
choke

1.
54
E5
wrought.
57
G5
A5
C5
D5
E
60
choke
65
choke
2.
70
E
wrought.
74
78

82
86
90
94
choke
97
choke
choke
99
102
105

107
E
C
D
3. Well_ I know they've al - ways_ told_ you_ self - ish-ness was_ wrong,
110
E
C
_ yet_ it was for_ me,_ not_ you_ I came
113
D
E
_ to write_ this song._
115
G
A
C
D
An - them of the heart and an - them of the mind, a fu - ne - ral_ dirge_ for
118
E
G
A
eyes gone blind. We mar - vel af - ter those who_ sought

121
C
Dadd11
C
Dadd11
C
Dadd11
won - ders in the world,
won - ders in the world,
won - ders in the world they
choke
choke
choke
124
E
G
D
wrought,
wrought,
wrought.
128
132
134
choke
137

CLOSER TO THE HEART

Music by Geddy Lee and Alex Lifeson
Lyrics by Neil Peart and Peter Talbot

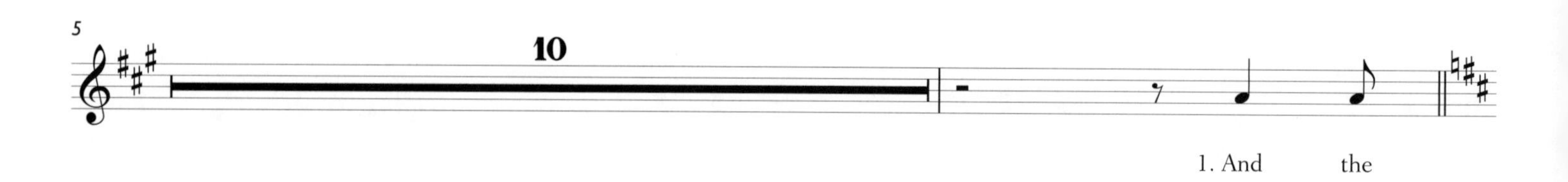

30
G
D
A
G
forge their cre - a - ti - vi - ty
clo - ser to the heart,
33
D
A
G
yes,
clo - ser to the heart.
36
N.C.
(glock/tubular bells)
3. Phi -
40
A5
G5
D
G5
A5
-lo - so - phers and plough - men,
each must know his part,
to
44
A5
G5
D
A5
G5
sow a new men - tal - i - ty
clo - ser to the heart,
yes,
48
D
A5
G5
D
A5
G5
clo - ser to the heart.
Yeah!
Woah!

GUITAR SOLO
52
D
G
C
Asus4
A
56
60
64
GUITAR RIFF
68
72
75
Aadd9
N.C.
Aadd9
Aadd9*
Amaj9
Aadd9
N.C.
4. Woah,

78
A5 G5 D G5 A
you can be the cap - tain, and I will draw the chart,
82
A5 G5 D A5 G
sail - ing in - to des - ti - ny, clo - ser to the heart,
86
D A5 G5 D A5 G5
clo - ser to the heart, clo - ser to the heart, yeah!
90
D A5 G5 D A5 G5
94
98
rall.

THE TEMPLES OF SYRINX

Music by Geddy Lee and Alex Lifeson
Lyrics by Neil Peart

17
G
A
N.C.
Bm
We are the priests of the temples of Syr - inx,
21
our great com- pu - ters fill the hal-lowed halls.
25
We are the priests of the tem - ples of Syr - inx,
29
D5
all the gifts of life are held with - in our walls.
33
36

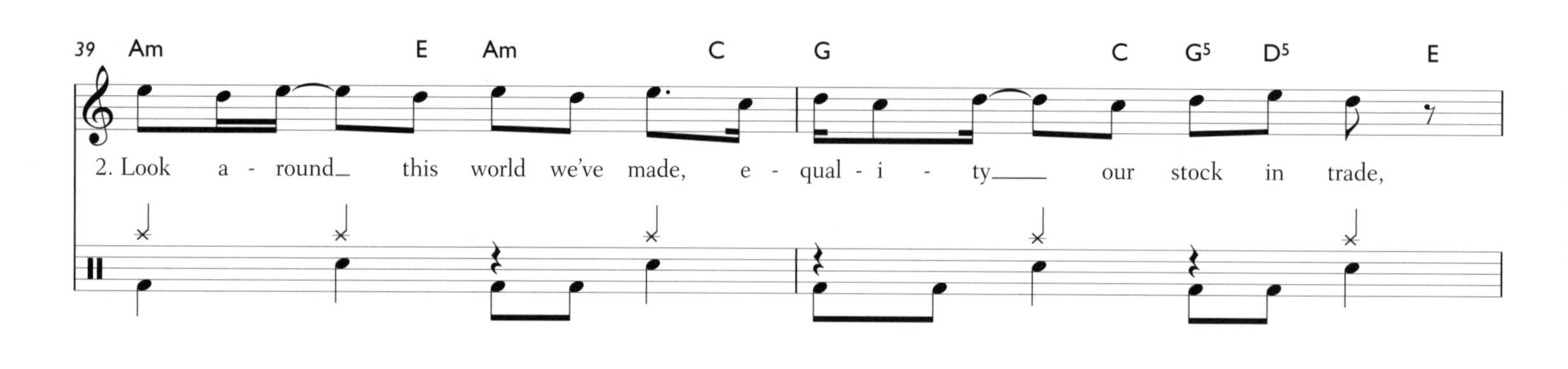
39
Am E Am C G C G5 D5 E
2. Look a - round_ this world we've made, e - qual - i - ty___ our stock in trade,

41
Am E Am C G E Am E Am C
come and join_ the broth - er - hood_ of man._ Oh what a nice_ con - ten - ted world,___
3 3

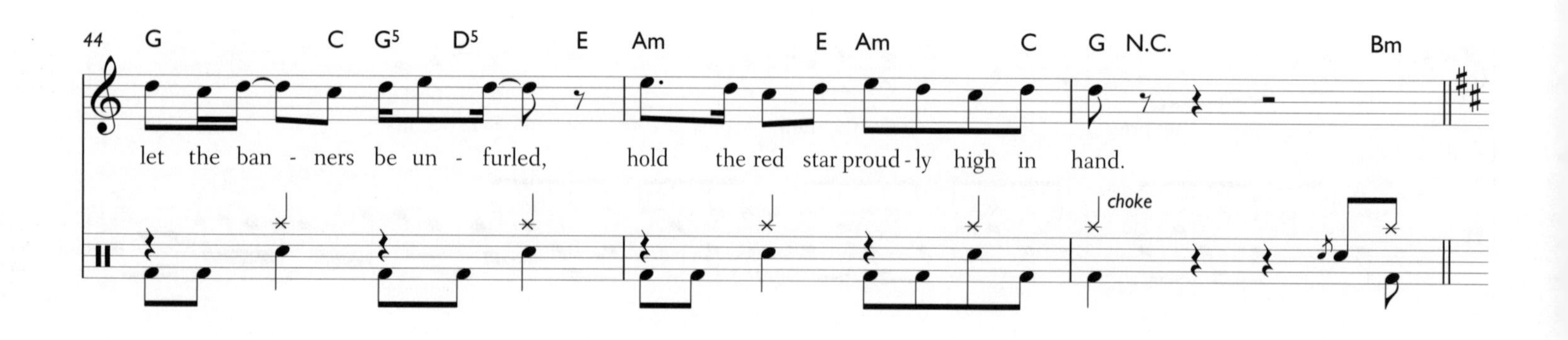
44
G C G5 D5 E Am E Am C G N.C. Bm
let the ban - ners be un - furled, hold the red star proud - ly high in hand.
choke

47
G A N.C.
We__ are__ the priests__ of the tem - ples of

50
Bm G A
Syr - inx, our__ great com - pu - ters fill__

53
N.C.
Bm
the hal-lowed halls.
6
6
6
55
G
A
N.C.
3
We are the priests of the tem-ples of
58
Bm
G
Syr - inx.
All the gifts of life
60
A
N.C.
D5
are held with - in our walls.
63
66
G
F♯
Bm
(classical gtr.)

TOM SAWYER

Music by Geddy Lee and Alex Lifeson
Lyrics by Neil Peart and Pye Dubois

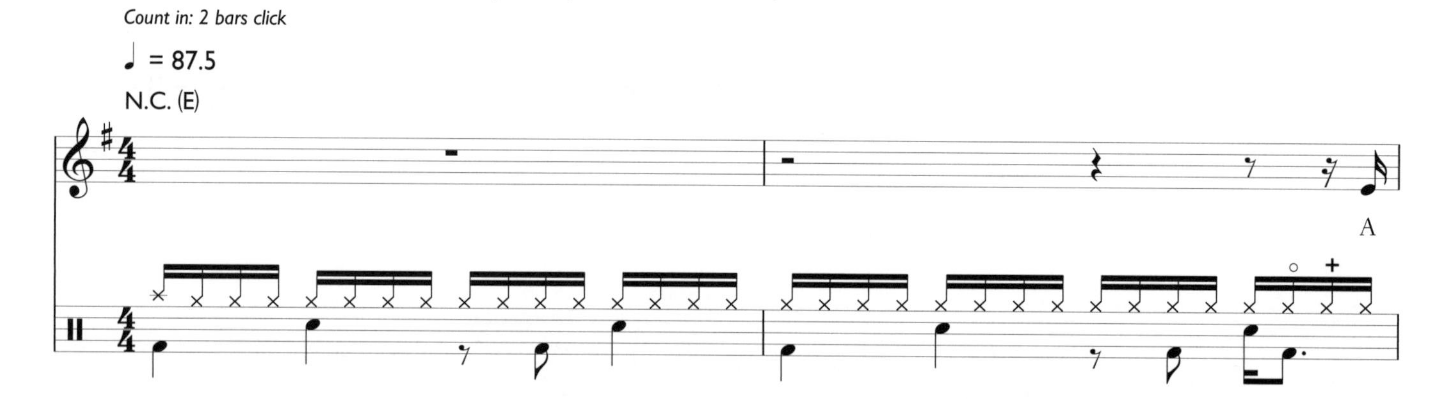

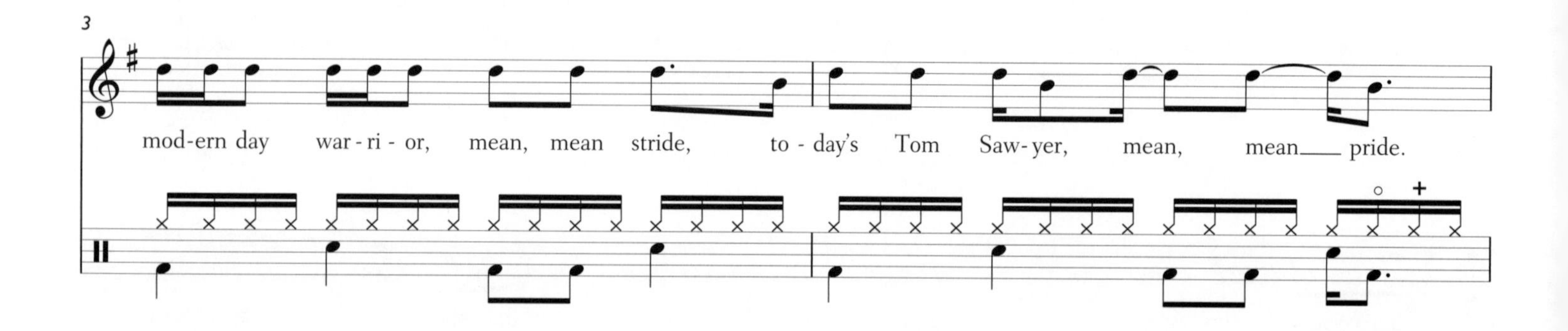

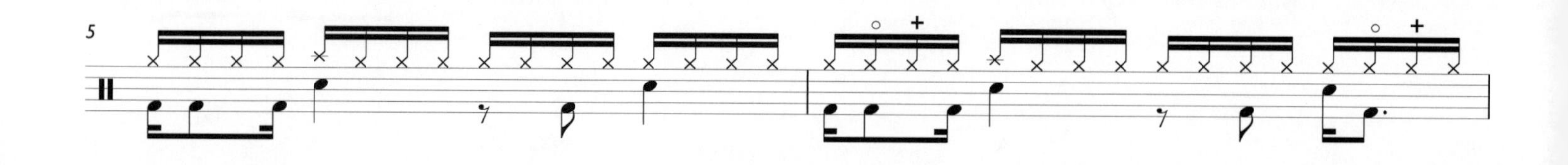

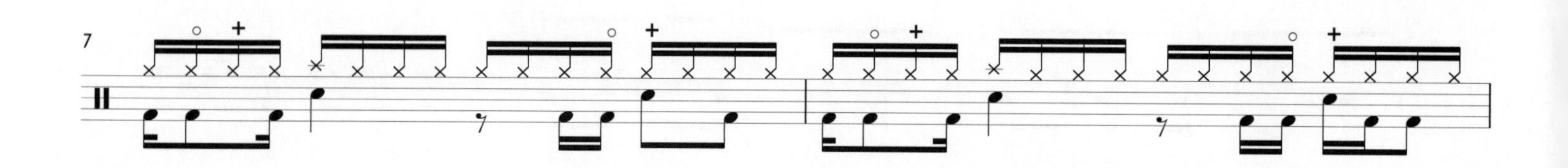

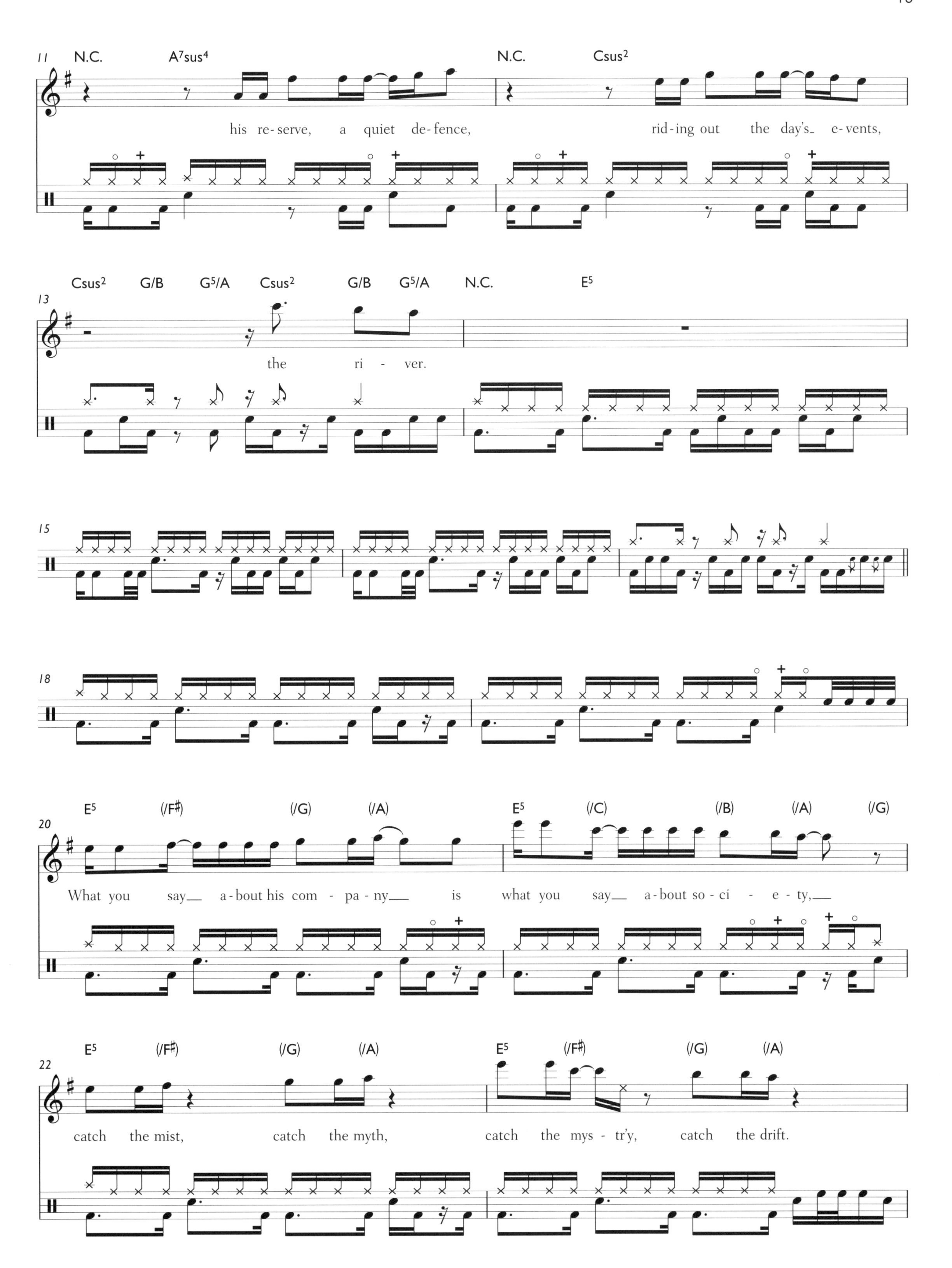
11
N.C.
A7sus4
N.C.
Csus2
his re-serve, a quiet de-fence,
rid-ing out the day's_ e-vents,
Csus2 G/B G5/A Csus2 G/B G5/A N.C. E5
13
the ri - ver.
15
18
E5 (/F♯) (/G) (/A) E5 (/C) (/B) (/A) (/G)
20
What you say__ a-bout his com - pa - ny__ is what you say__ a-bout so - ci - e - ty,__
E5 (/F♯) (/G) (/A) E5 (/F♯) (/G) (/A)
22
catch the mist, catch the myth, catch the mys - tr'y, catch the drift.

E5
(/C)
(/B)
(/A)
(/G)
E5
(/F♯)
(/G)
(/A)
24
26
Bsus2
A5
Gsus2
B5
HH (open)
The world is, the world_ is, love and life are deep,
29
A5
Gsus2
A5
_ may - be as his eyes are
31
E5
wide. To -
33
- day's Tom Saw-yer, he gets high on you,_ and the space he in - vades, he gets by_ on you.

SYNTH SOLO
35
39
43
GUITAR SOLO
46
*click muted in all x/16 bars!
50
54
57

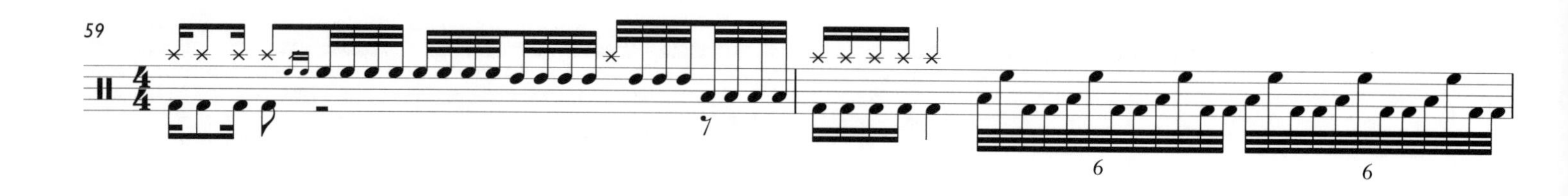
59
6
6

61

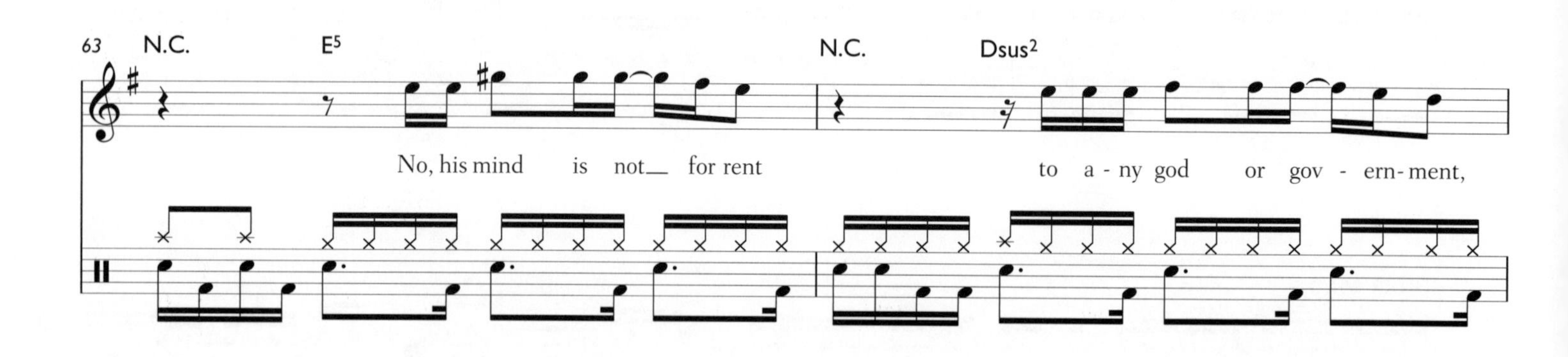
63
N.C.
E5
No, his mind is not__ for rent
N.C.
Dsus2
to a - ny god or gov - ern - ment,

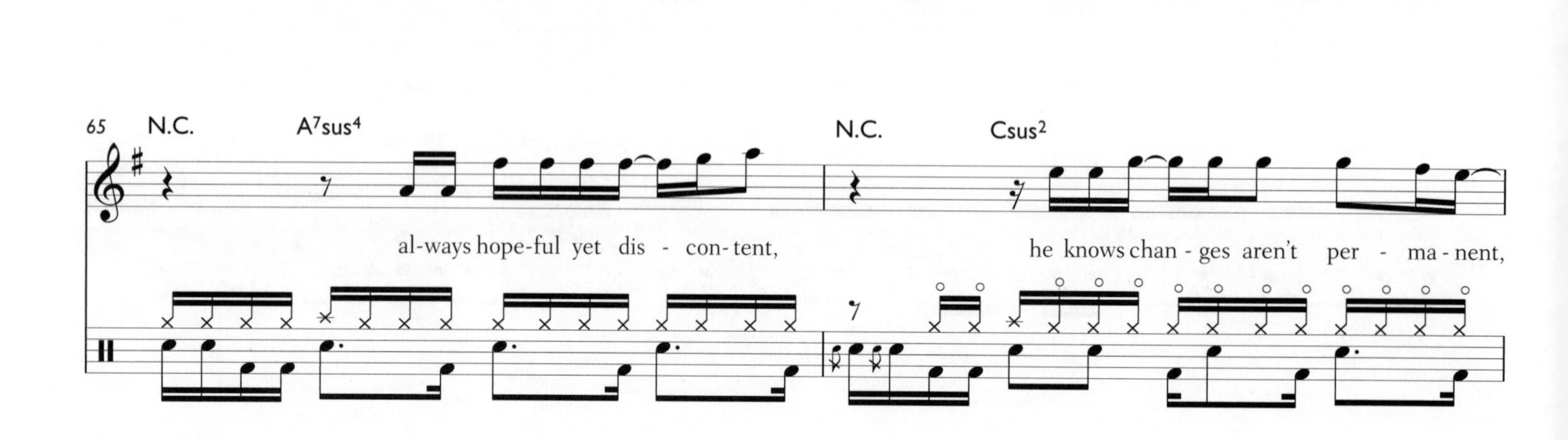
65
N.C.
A7sus4
al-ways hope-ful yet dis - con - tent,
N.C.
Csus2
he knows chan - ges aren't per - ma - nent,

67
Csus2
G/B
G5/A
Csus2
G/B
G5/A
N.C.
E5
but change is.

69
71
72
E5
And
74
E5
(/F♯)
(/G)
(/A)
E5
(/C)
(/B)
(/A)
(/G)
what you say a-bout his com - pa - ny is what you say a-bout so - ci - e - ty,
6
76
E5
(/F♯)
(/G)
(/A)
E5
(/C)
(/B)
(/A)
(/G)
catch the wit-ness, catch the wit, catch the spi - rit, catch the spit.
3
3
78
3
3

80
Bsus2
A5
Gsus2
B5
The world is, the world_ is, love and life are deep,
HH (open)
83
A5
Gsus2
A5
— may - be as his eyes are
85
E5
wide.
87
Ex - it the war - ri - or, to - day's Tom Saw - yer, he gets high on you_ and the en - er - gy you trade, he gets
89
E5
F♯5
E5
F♯5
right on to the fric - tion of_ the day.

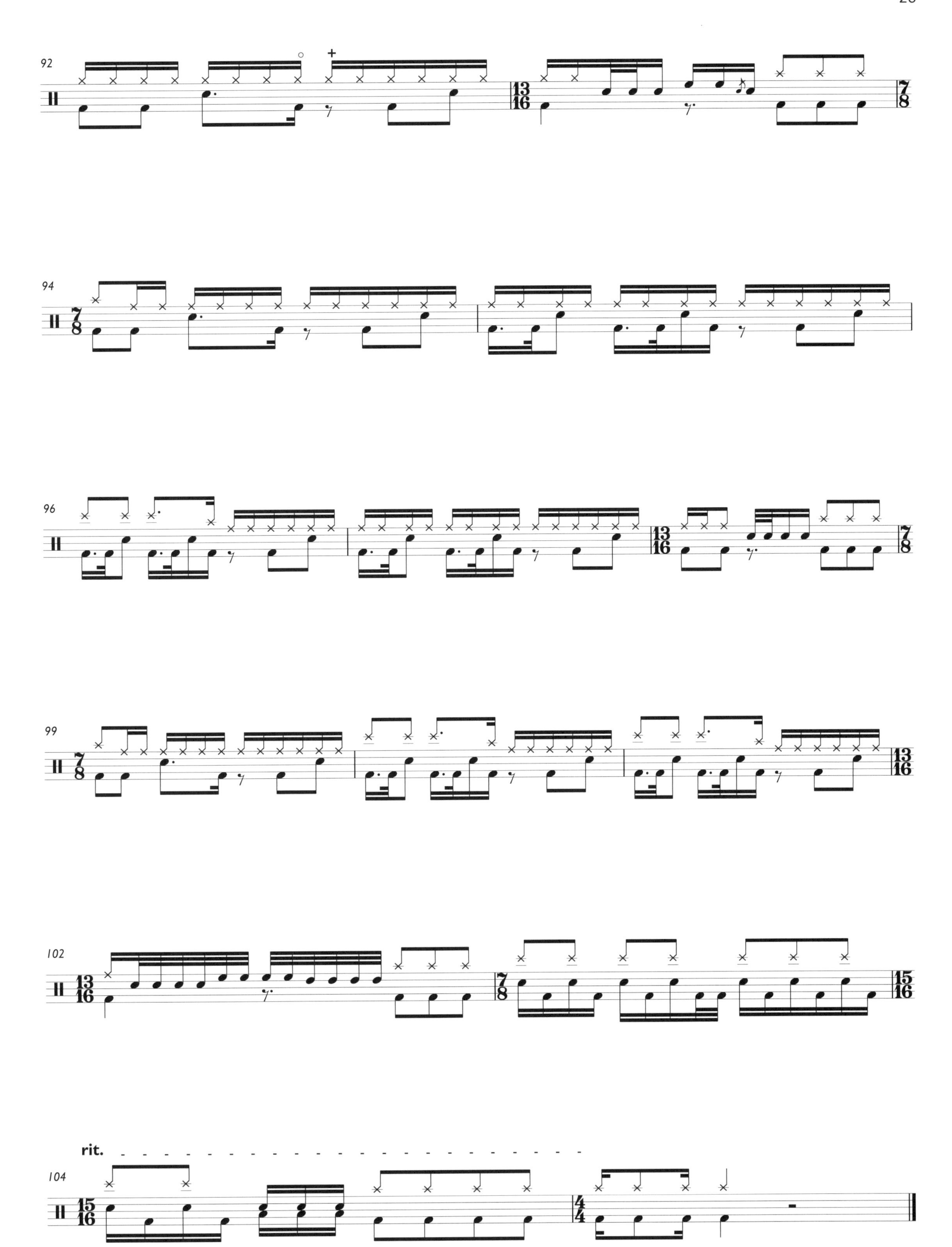
92
94
96
99
102
104
rit.

YYZ

Music by Geddy Lee and Neil Peart

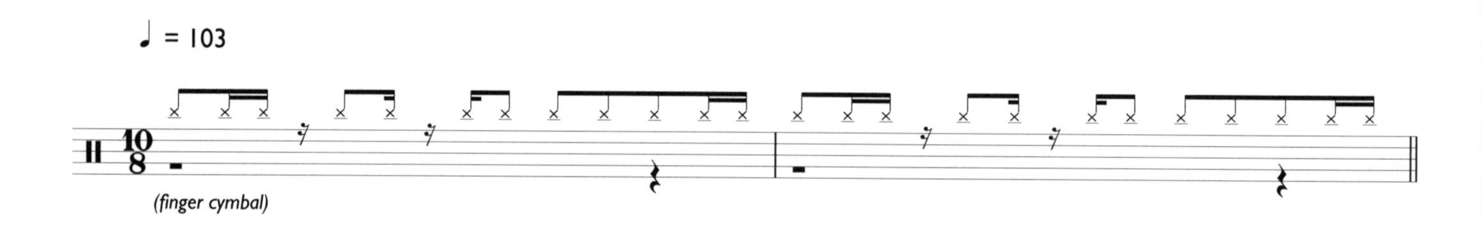

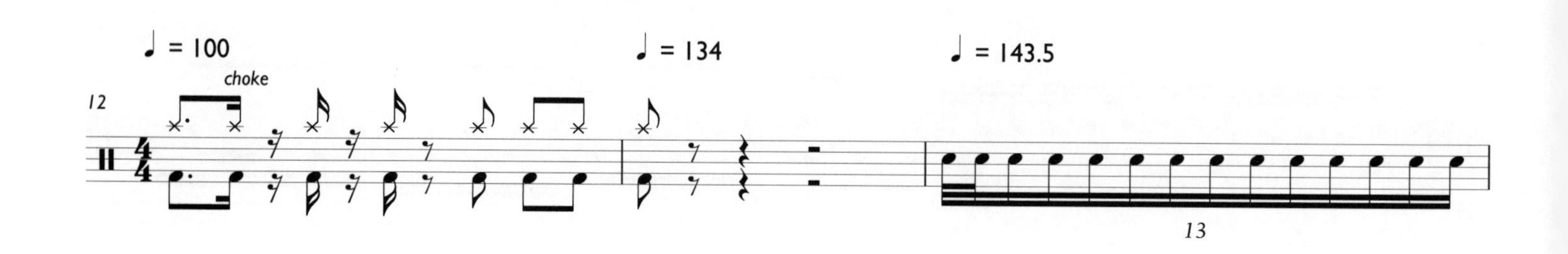

♩ = 140
MAIN RIFF
19
23
27
31
35
ride bell
39
43
ride bell

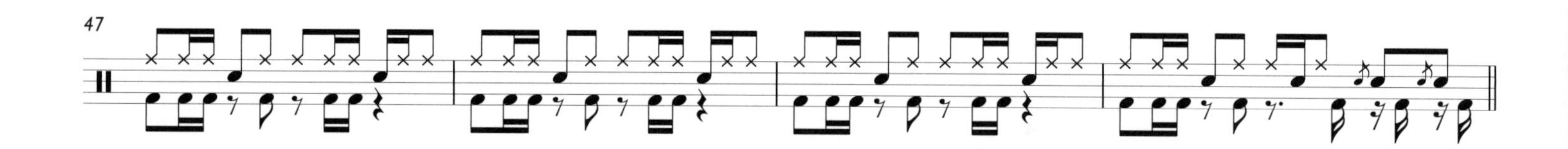
47

BASS RIFF
51
(bass break)

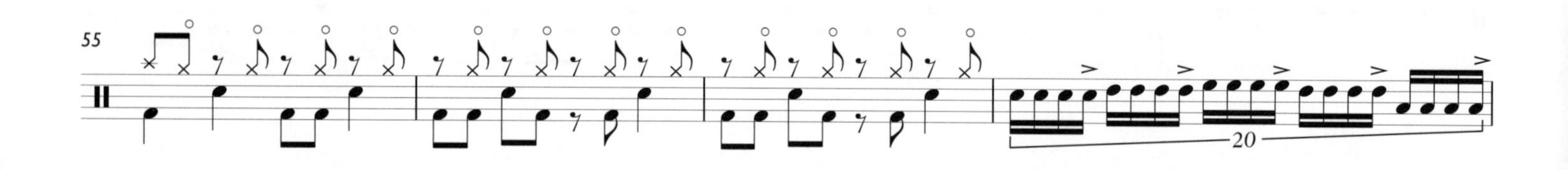
55
20

59
(bass break)

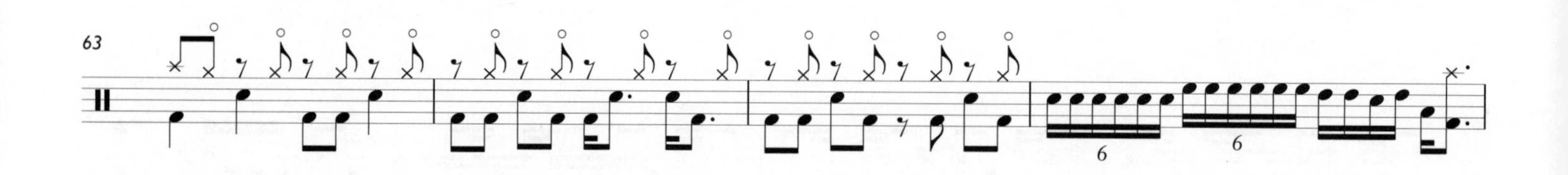
63
6
6

67
(bass break)

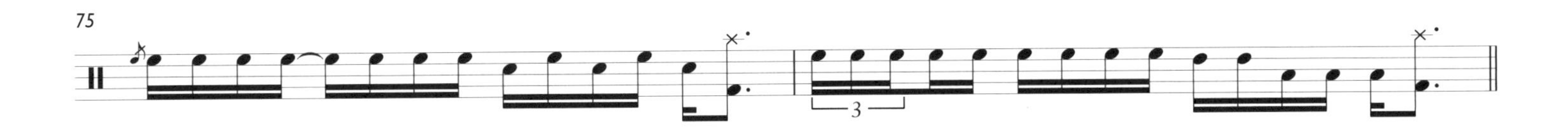

GUITAR SOLO

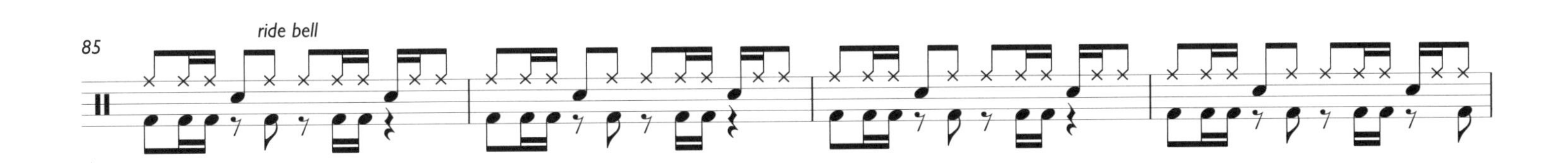

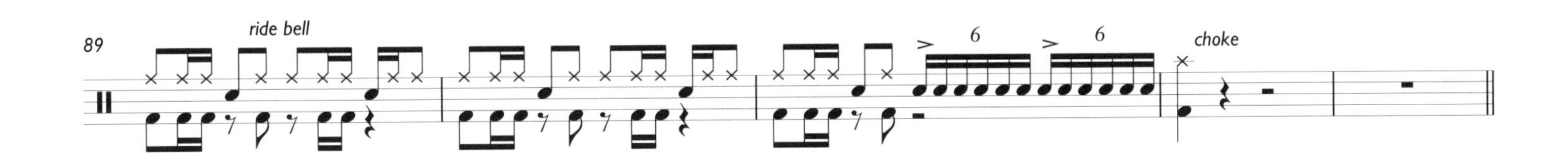

MIDDLE

98

102

106
3

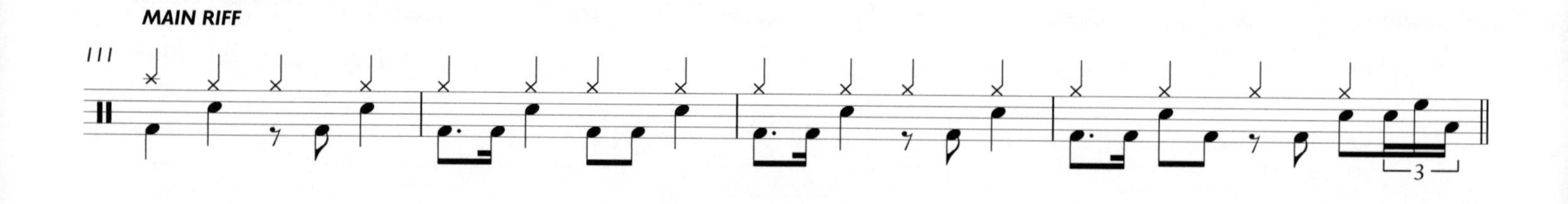
MAIN RIFF
111
3

115

119
3
3

123

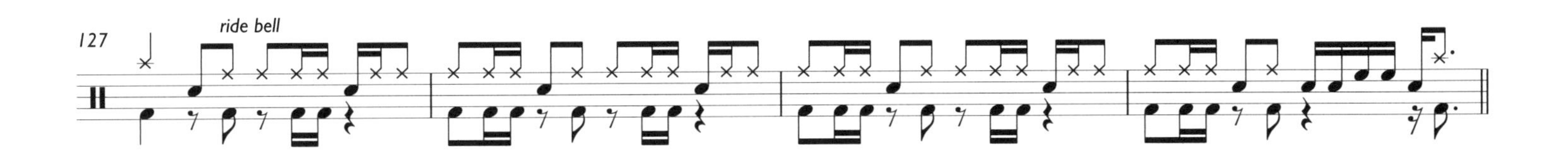
127
ride bell

131
ride bell

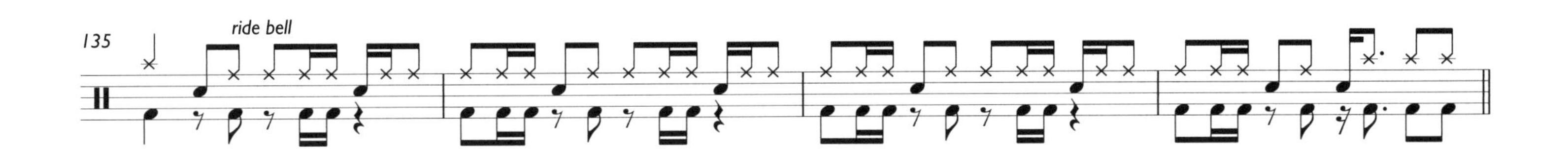
135
ride bell

139
ride bell
3
6

♩ = 103
142
5
5
5
5
10
8
7
8

THE SPIRIT OF RADIO

Music by Geddy Lee and Alex Lifeson
Lyrics by Neil Peart

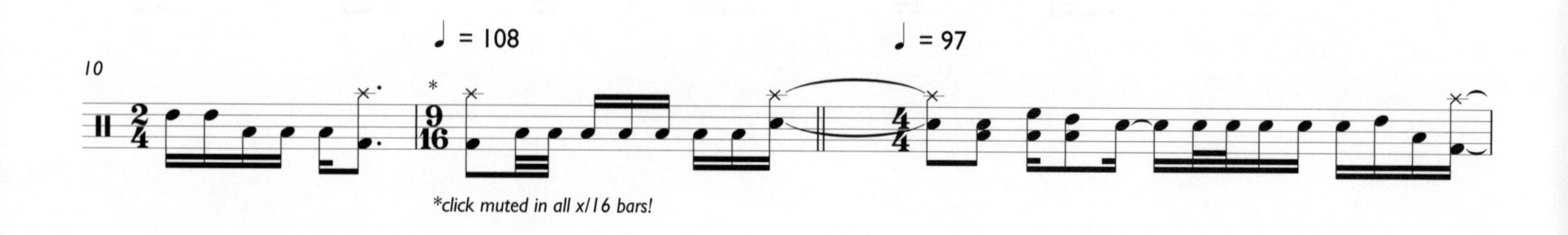

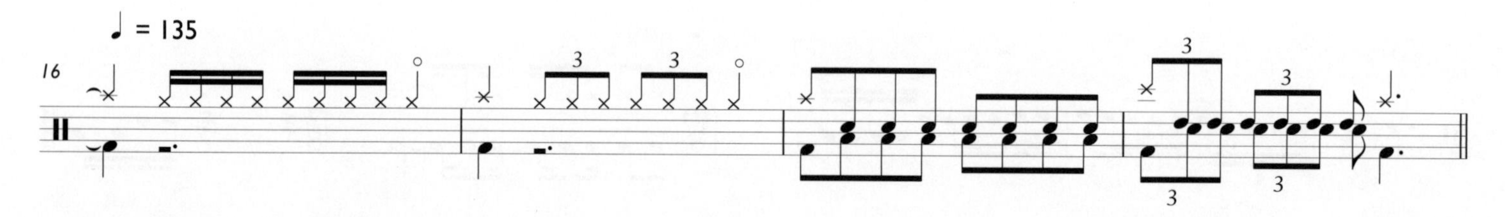

20
E5
Badd11
E/G♯
A
B
Be-
24
E5
Badd11
E/G♯
-gin the day with a friend - ly voice, a com-pan - ion un - ob - tru-
27
A
B
E5
Badd11
- sive. Plays that song that's so e - lu - sive and the
30
E/G♯
A
B
E5
ma - gic mus - ic makes your morn - ing mood.
33
Badd11
E/G♯
A
B

36
E
B
E/G♯
Off on your way, hit the op - en road, there is ma - gic at your fin -
39
A
B
E
B
- gers. For the spi - rit ev - er lin - gers, un - de -
42
E/G♯
A
B
- mand - ing con - tact in your hap - py so - li - tude.
44
48
E5
In -

52
(D/F♯)
(E/G♯)
-vi - si - ble air - ways crac - kle with life,
bright an - ten - nae bris -
55
(D/F♯)
(E5)
- tle with the en - er - gy.
E -
58
(D/F♯)
(E/G♯)
- mo - tion - al feed - back on a time - less wave - length,
bear - ing a gift be - yond
61
(D/F♯)
(E5)
price: al - most free.
64
E5
B
E/G♯
A
B
All this mach-in - er - y mak-ing mod-ern mus - ic can still be op - en heart - ed.

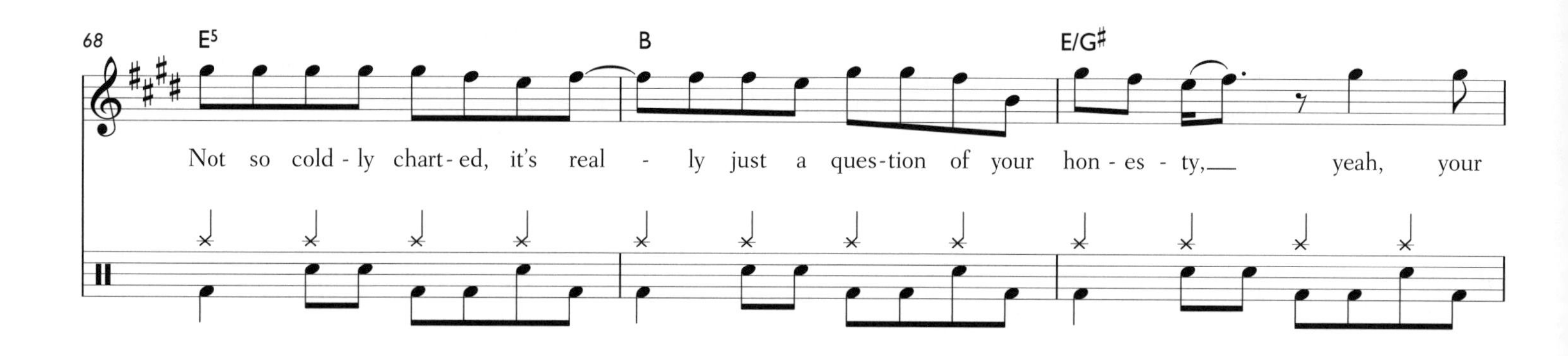
68
E5
B
E/G#
Not so cold-ly chart-ed, it's real - ly just a ques-tion of your hon-es-ty, yeah, your

71
A
B
E5
B
hon-es-ty. One likes to be-lieve in the free-dom of mus-

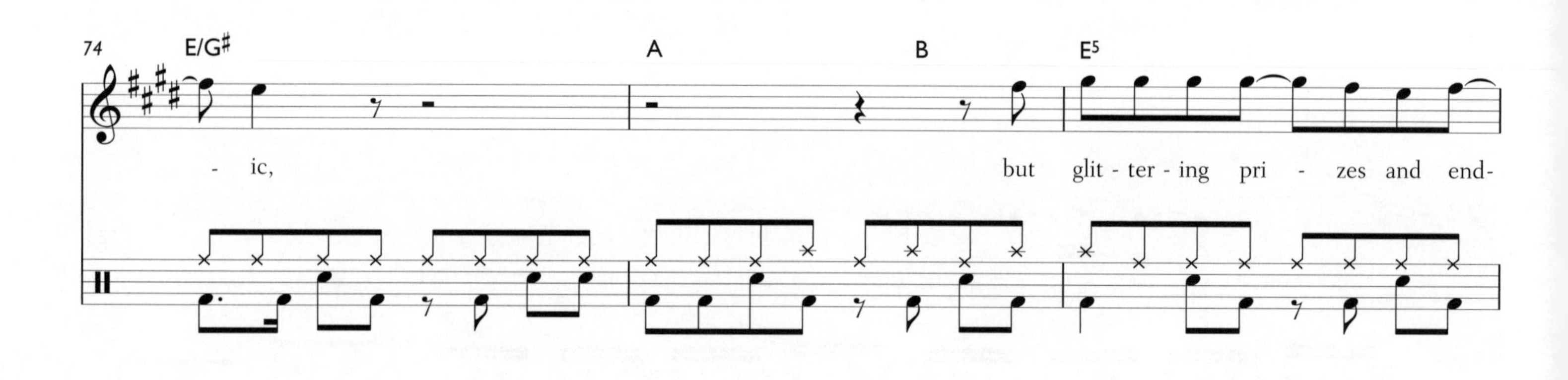
74
E/G#
A
B
E5
- ic, but glit-ter-ing pri - zes and end-

77
B
E/G#
A
B
- less com-pro-mis-es shat-ter the il-lus-ion of in - te-gri - ty, yeah.

80
84
E5
In -
88
(D/F♯)
(E/G♯)
-vi - si - ble air - ways crac - kle with life,
bright an - ten - nae bris -
91
(D/F♯)
(E5)
- tle with the en - er - gy.
E -
94
(D/F♯)
- mo - tion - al feed - back on a time - less wave - length,
HH (half open)

96
(E/G#)
(D/F#)
bear - ing a gift be - yond price: al - most
98
E5
D/F#
free.
100
103
105
108
112

♩ = 108
116
♩ = 91
120
♩ = 74.5
122
E A B
For the
125
E A B E A B
words of the pro-fits were writ-ten on the stu-di-o wall,
con-cert hall.
♩ = 78
127
E5 A5 E5 A5
129
E A B E A B
And ech-oes with the sound of sales-

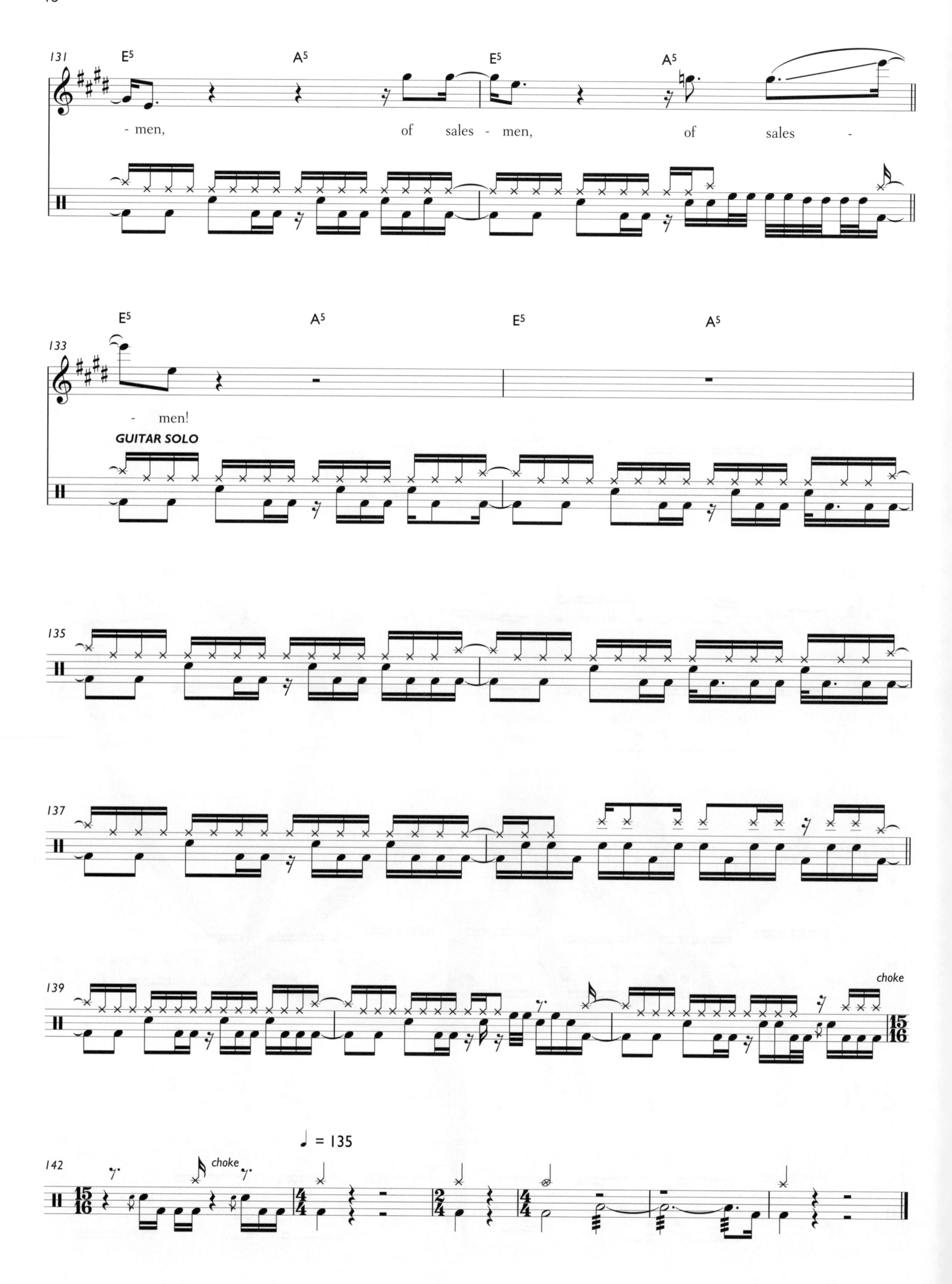
131
E5
A5
E5
A5
- men,
of
sales - men,
of
sales -
E5
A5
E5
A5
133
- men!
GUITAR SOLO
135
137
139
choke
142
choke
♩ = 135

DRUM CHARTS

ANTHEM

Music and Lyrics by Geddy Lee, Alex Lifeson and Neil Peart

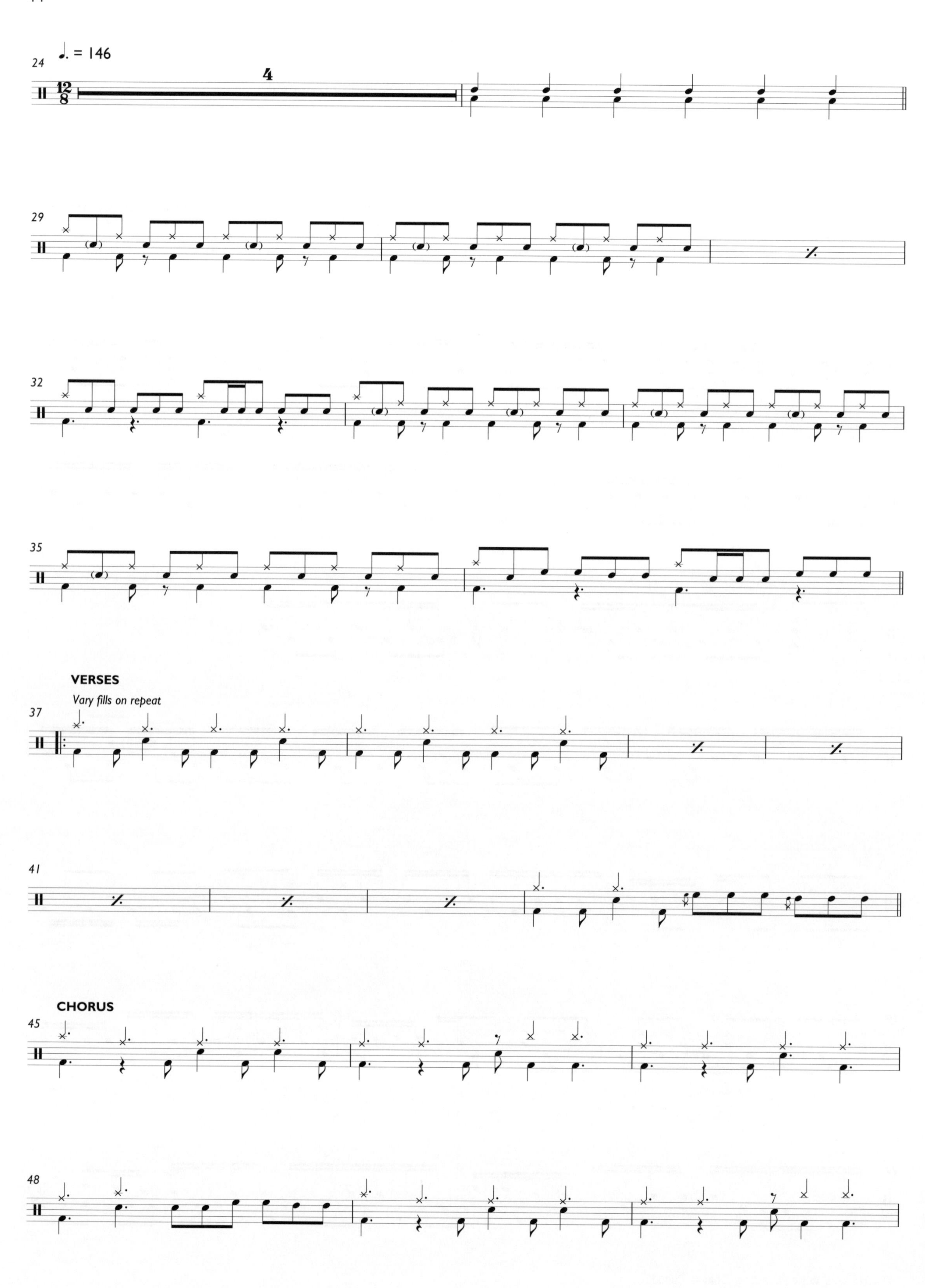
♩. = 146
24
4
29
32
35
VERSES
Vary fills on repeat
37
41
CHORUS
45
48

51
choke
choke
choke
1.
54
G5
A5
C5
D5
E
57
60
choke
65
choke
2.
70
74
78

82
86
90
94
choke
99
102
105
VERSE 3
107

110
113
CHORUS 3
115
118
121
choke
choke
choke
124
130
134
choke
137

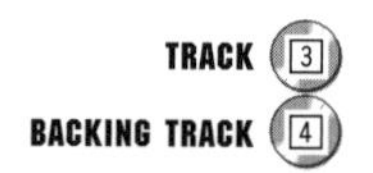

CLOSER TO THE HEART

Music by Geddy Lee and Alex Lifeson
Lyrics by Neil Peart and Peter Talbot

60
64
GUITAR RIFF
68
72
75
VERSE 4
78
82
86
90
94
98
rall.

THE TEMPLES OF SYRINX

Music by Geddy Lee and Alex Lifeson
Lyrics by Neil Peart

VERSE 2
39
3
3
43
choke
CHORUS 2
47
50
53
6
6
6
55
58
60
63
66
G
F♯
Bm
(classical gtr.)

TOM SAWYER

Music by Geddy Lee and Alex Lifeson
Lyrics by Neil Peart and Pye Dubois

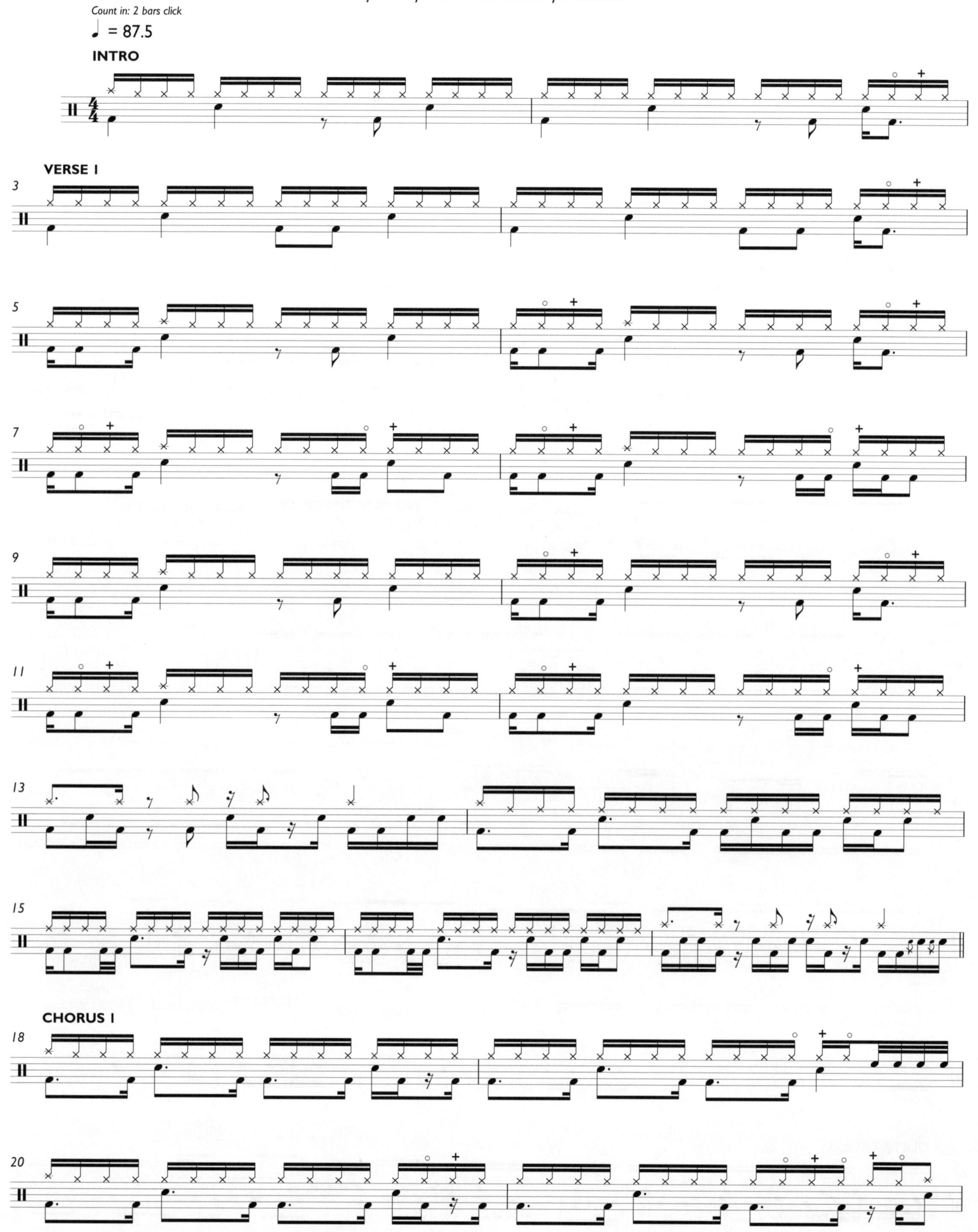

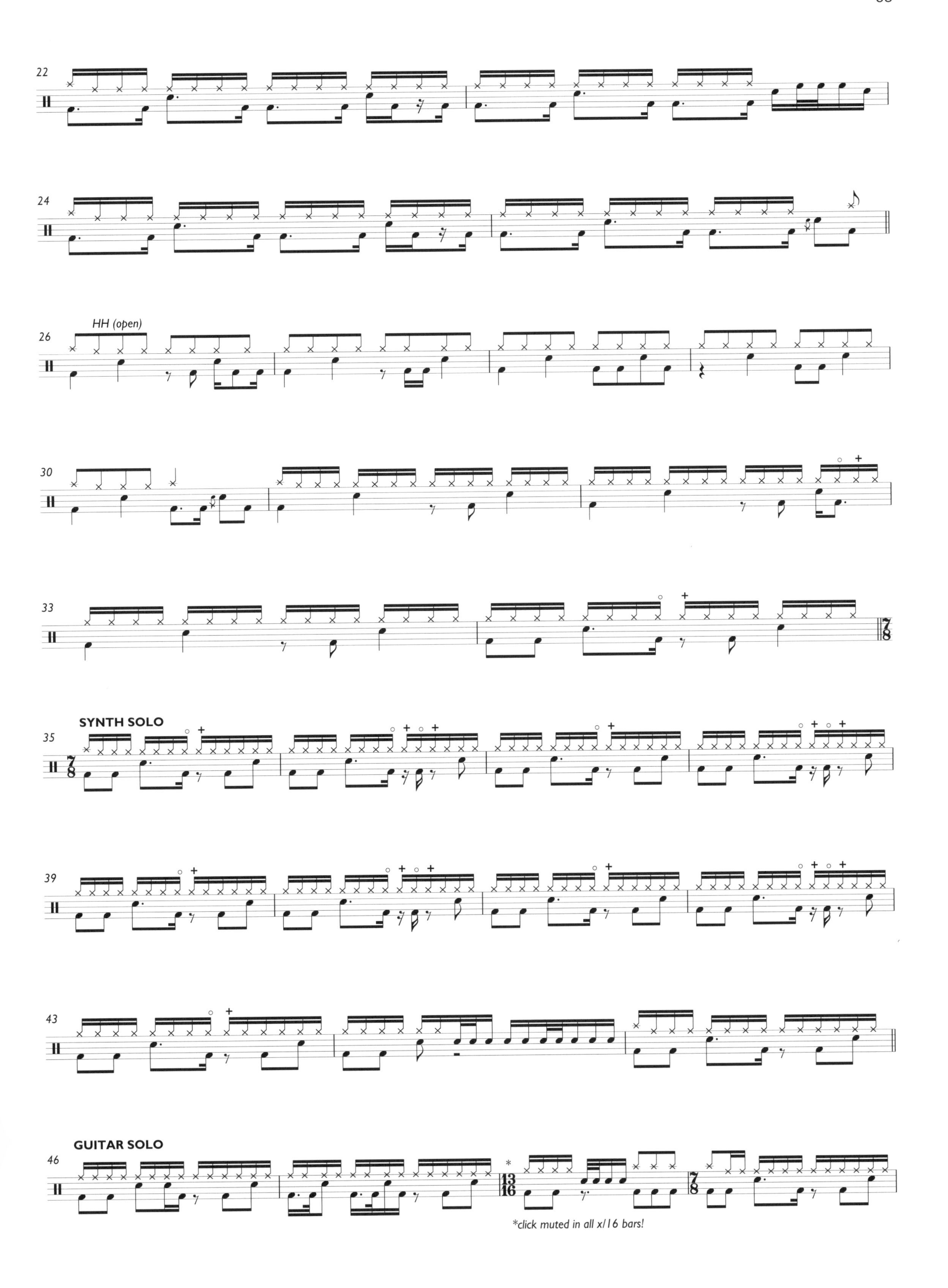

22
24
HH (open)
26
30
33
SYNTH SOLO
35
39
43
GUITAR SOLO
46
*click muted in all x/16 bars!

50
54
57
59
61
63
65
67
69
71

CHORUS
72
74
6
77
3
3
3
3
80
HH (open)
84
VERSE 3
87
OUTRO
90
94
97
100
rit.
103

YYZ

Music by Geddy Lee and Neil Peart

31
35
ride bell
39
43
ride bell
47
BASS RIFF
51
(bass break)
55
20
59
(bass break)
63
6
6
67
(bass break)

72
75
GUITAR SOLO
ride bell
77
81
ride bell
85
ride bell
89
ride bell
choke
MIDDLE
94
98
102
106

MAIN RIFF
111
115
119
123
127
ride bell
131
ride bell
135
ride bell
139
ride bell
142
♩ = 103

THE SPIRIT OF RADIO

Music by Geddy Lee and Alex Lifeson
Lyrics by Neil Peart

VERSE 2
36
39
42
45
48
52
CHORUS
58
VERSE 3
64
69
73
76

80
84
88
CHORUS 2
94
HH (half open)
98
INSTRUMENTAL
100
103
105
108
112
116
♩ = 108

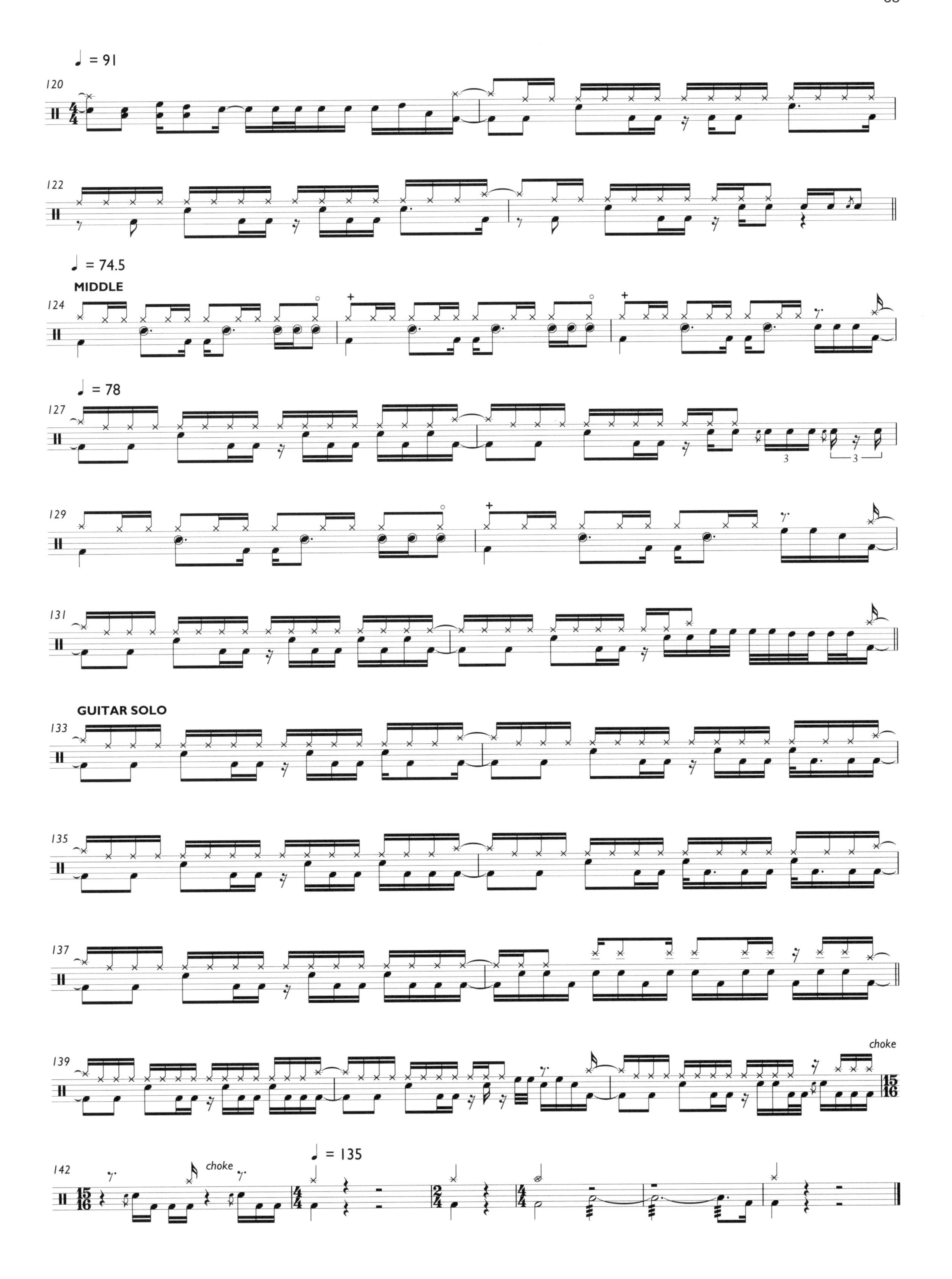
♩ = 91
120
122
♩ = 74.5
MIDDLE
124
♩ = 78
127
3
3
129
131
GUITAR SOLO
133
135
137
139
choke
142
choke
♩ = 135